Zaner-Bloser Handwriting

PRACTICE MASTERS

2M

Illustrations by Josh Hara

© 2020 Zaner-Bloser, Inc. All rights reserved.

ISBN 978-1-4531-1945-7

This book is printed on paper certified by third-party standards for sustainably managed forestry.

Zaner-Bloser, Inc.
800.421.3018
zaner-bloser.com

Printed in the United States of America   1 2 3 4 5 6 7 8 9 10 23975 23 22 21 20 19 18   ZB Code 20

Contents

Practice Masters

Guidelines 1
Writing Positions:
   Left-Handed Writers 2
Writing Positions:
   Right-Handed Writers 3
Basic Strokes: Vertical Lines 4
Basic Strokes: Horizontal Lines 5
Basic Strokes: Circle Lines 6
Basic Strokes: Diagonal Lines 7
Basic Strokes Review 8
Keys to Legibility 9
Numerals 10
l, i, t 14
L, I, T 17
o, a, d 20
O, A, D 23
c, e, f 26
C, E, F 29
g, j, q 32
G, J, Q 35
u, s 38
U, S 40
b, p, r 42
B, P, R 45
n, m, h 48
N, M, H 51
v, y, w 54
V, Y, W 57
x, k, z 60
X, K, Z 63

Additional Home Practice

l, i, t 66
L, I, T 67
o, a, d 68
O, A, D 69
c, e, f 70
C, E, F 71
g, j, q 72
G, J, Q 73
u, s 74
U, S 75
b, p, r 76
B, P, R 77
n, m, h 78
N, M, H 79
v, y, w 80
V, Y, W 81
x, k, z 82
X, K, Z 83

Support Materials

Record of Student's Handwriting Skills . . 84
Certificate of Excellence 85
Certificate of Progress 86
Manuscript Alphabet 87
Manuscript Letter and Numeral
   Formations 88
Handwriting Grid 92
Story-Writing Grid 93

Name: _____

Guidelines

Headline

Midline

Baseline

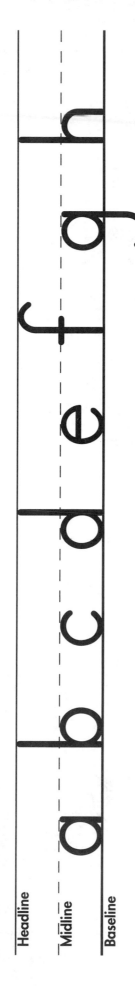

a b c d e f g h

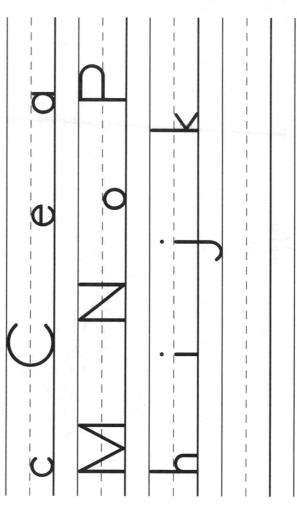

c C e a

M N o P

h i j k

Which letter is tall? Circle it.

Which letter is short? Circle it.

Which letter goes below the baseline? Circle it.

Write a word that has both tall and short letters.

Writing Positions

If you write with your **left hand**, follow the rules on this page.

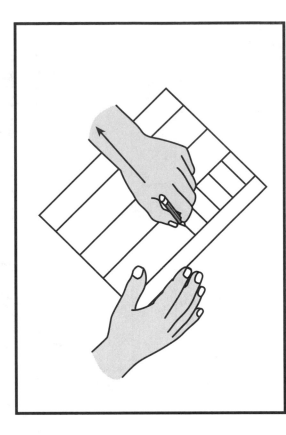

Slant your paper as shown in the picture.
Rest both arms on the desk. Use your right hand to move the paper as you write.
Pull the pencil toward your left elbow when you write.

Digital Tutor
Paper Position

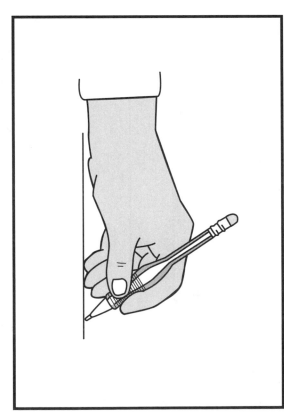

Hold the pencil with your thumb and first two fingers.
Do not squeeze the pencil when you write.

Digital Tutor
Pencil Position

Writing Positions

If you write with your **right hand**, follow the rules on this page.

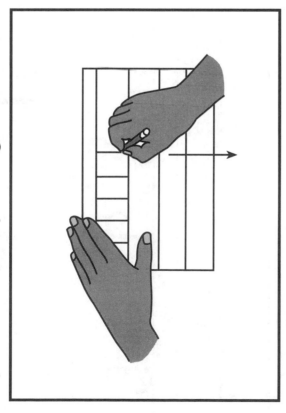

Place the paper straight in front of you.

Rest both arms on the desk. Use your left hand to move the paper as you write.

Pull the pencil toward the middle of your body when you write.

Digital Tutor

Paper Position

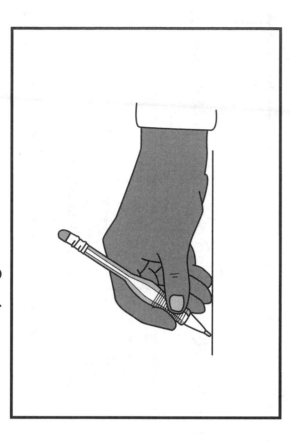

Hold the pencil with your thumb and first two fingers.

Do not squeeze the pencil when you write.

Digital Tutor

Pencil Position

Practice Master 3

Basic Strokes: Vertical Lines

Trace the vertical lines in these letters and numerals.

D K N P I t h i b g 4 5

Write the pull down straight lines. Start at the dot.

Write the push up straight lines.

Name: _____

Basic Strokes: Horizontal Lines

Trace the horizontal lines in these letters and numerals.

A F H E G e f t z 4 7 2 5

Write the slide right lines. Start at the dot.

Write the slide left lines.

Name: _____

Basic Strokes: Circle Lines

Trace a circle or part of a circle in these letters and numerals.

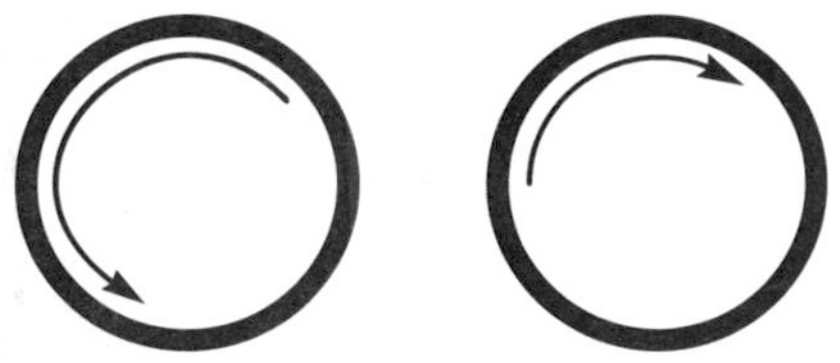

O G R B g p 6 9

Write the circle back lines. Start at the dot.

Write the circle forward lines.

Name: _____

Basic Strokes: Diagonal Lines

Trace the diagonal lines in these letters and numerals.

A Z X y k 2 7

Write the slant right lines. Start at the dot.

Write the slant left lines.

Write the slant up lines.

Name: _____

Basic Strokes Review

Write these lines.

Draw a picture using four kinds of lines.

Keys to Legibility

Shape
Digital Tutor | Shape

Shape Look at the shape of these letters. Trace the letters.

t i G Q K

Manuscript letters contain vertical lines (l), horizontal lines (—), circle lines (O C Ɔ), and diagonal lines (\ /).

Size
Digital Tutor | Size

Size Look at the size of these letters. Trace the letters.

A b c e p

Tall letters touch the headline. Short letters touch the midline. Letters with descenders go below the baseline and touch the next headline.

Spacing
Digital Tutor | Spacing

Spacing Look at the spacing in this writing. Trace the words.

a good book

The letters are neither too close together nor too far apart.

There is enough space for your finger between words.

Slant
Digital Tutor | Slant

Slant Look at the vertical slant of this writing. Trace the word.

letters

Manuscript letters are straight up and down. To write with good slant:

1. Place your paper correctly.
2. Pull down in the proper direction.
3. Shift your paper as you write.

Name: _____

Numerals

Write the numerals and number sentences.

1 _____

2 _____

3 _____

1 _____ 2 _____

2 _____ 3 _____

3 _____ 4 _____

4 _____ 5 _____

5 _____

3 + 2 = 5 _____ 4 − 3 = 1 _____

Write a number sentence. Use + or −.

_____

_____

Name: _____

Numerals

Write the numerals and number sentences.

6   7   8   9   10

6   7   8   9   10

10 − 8 = 2   9 − 6 = 3

Write a number sentence. Use **+** or **−**.

_____

Name: _____

Numeral Review

Write the number sentences.

$1 + 8 = 9$

$2 + 7 = 9$

$5 - 4 = 1$

$3 - 2 = 1$

Write number sentences. Use + and −.

Name: _____

Numeral Application

Write the times on the digital clocks.

2:59   **9:43**   **6:17**

_____   _____   _____

8:00   **12:30**   **4:56**

_____   _____   _____

Write numerals to tell what time you wake up on a school day.

_____

Name:

Digital Tutor

Letter Model and Formation

Write the letters and words.

l l l l l l l l

light little lift late

list lion life level

lick lots of lollipops

Home Practice **Letter Formation**

1. Pull down straight.

Name:

Write the letters and words.

| | | | | | | |

idea   into   itch   inside

invite   island   itself   indoor

nine inches wide

Letter
Formation

1. Pull down straight. Lift.
2. Dot.

Home
Practice

Name: _____

Write the letters and words.

t t t t t t

ten   thin   tear

tiny   toad   travel   twig

tie too tight

Home
Practice

Letter
Formation

1. Pull down straight. Lift.
2. Slide right.

Name: _____

Write the letters and sentences.

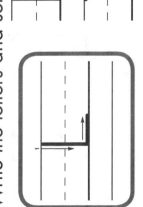

Leon lives near Lucy.

Lucy visited Leon.

Let's go to Lee's!

Letter
Formation

Home
Practice

1. Pull down straight. Slide right.

Name: _____

Write the letters and sentences.

I   I   I   I   I   I   I

I man and I like to ice-skate.

Ice-skating is fun!

I glide across the ice.

1. Pull down straight. Lift.
2. Slide right. Lift.
3. Slide right.

Name: _____

Write the letters and sentences.

Tamar took us to Tampa.

Tampa is too hot!

Tomorrow we go to Tempe.

Letter
Formation

1. Pull down straight. Lift.
2. Slide right.

Home
Practice

Digital Tutor

Letter Model and Formation

Name:

Write the letters and words.

o

o o o o o o o

ocean office once oil

own order onto orange

our old oven

Home Practice

Letter Formation

o

1. Circle back all the way around.

Name:

Write the letters and words.

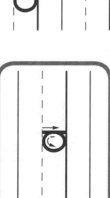

a a a a a

a a a a a

. .

across   afraid   alike

arm   arrow   art

apart

an angry ant

Home
Practice

Letter
Formation

1. Circle back all the way around; push up
straight. Pull down straight.

Name:

Digital Tutor

Letter Model and Formation

Write the letters and words.

d

d d d d d d d

dash dear desk doll

drum deep done dream

dirty, dusty dog

Home Practice

Letter Formation

d

1. Circle back all the way around; push up straight. Pull down straight.

Name: _____

Write the letters and sentences.

Omar hiked the Oregon Trail.

Olga lives on October Street.

Omar is older than Olga.

Digital Tutor

Letter Model and Formation

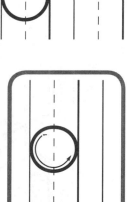

Letter Formation

1. Circle back all the way around.

Home Practice

Practice Master 23

Name:

Digital Tutor
Letter Model and Formation

Write the letters and sentences.

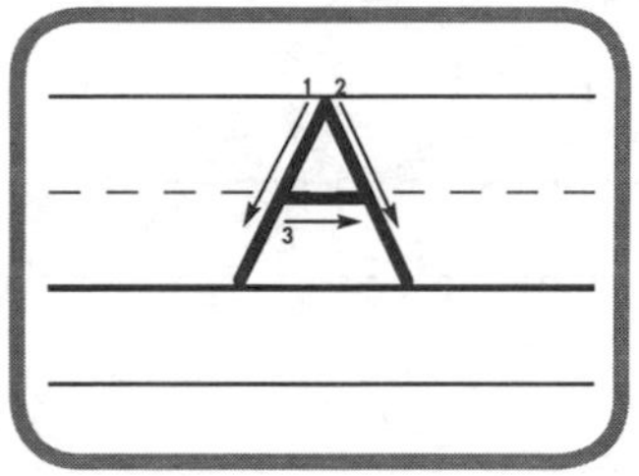

A A A A A A

Mrs. Adams asked a question.

Asa answered Mrs. Adams.

Amy agreed with Asa.

Home Practice **Letter Formation**

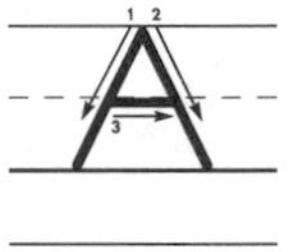

1. Slant left. Lift.
2. Slant right. Lift.
3. Slide right.

Name: _____

Write the letters and sentences.

D D D D D D

Dustin drove to Denver.

Didi invited Dustin to dinner.

Does she cook noodles?

© Zaner-Bloser, Inc.

Digital Tutor

Letter Model and Formation

Letter Formation

1. Pull down straight. Lift.
2. Slide right; curve forward; slide left.

Home Practice

Name: _____

Write the letters and words.

C   C   C   C   C   C

cage   center   chase   cup

.   .

cool   crash   clue   circus

chewy candy corn

1. Circle back.

© Zaner-Bloser, Inc.

Name: _____

Write the letters and words.

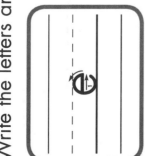

e e e e e e e

e e e e e

e . .

earth   edge   enemy   empty

enter   except   easy   end

eighty-eight cents

1. Slide right. Circle back.

Home Practice

Letter Formation e

Name: _____

Write the letters and words.

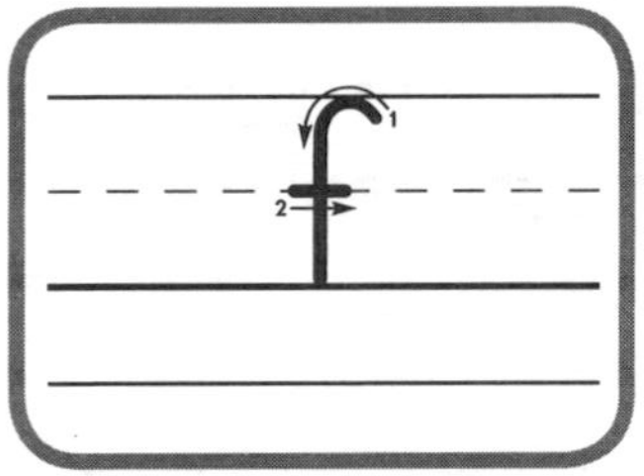

f   f   f   f   f   f

f   f   f   f   f   f

fact

farm

field

float

free

front

fair

fence

flat feet first

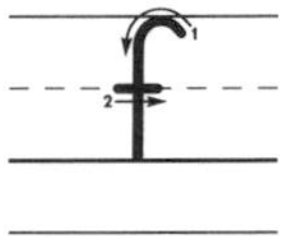

_____

Practice Master 28

© Zaner-Bloser, Inc.

Name:

Write the letters and sentences.

C C C C C C C

Chip called Cline.

Chet took a cab to Charlotte.

Cline met Chet.

Digital Tutor

Letter Model
and Formation

Home Practice

Letter Formation

1. Circle back.

Name: _____

Write the letters and sentences.

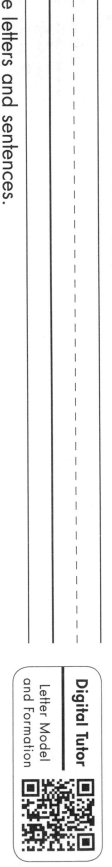

E E E E E E

E E E E E E

Eve wants to go to England.

Eddie ended up in New England.

Everyone missed Eddie.

Letter
Formation

1. Pull down straight. Lift.
2. Slide right. Lift.
3. Slide right; stop short. Lift.
4. Slide right.

Name: _____

Digital Tutor

Letter Model and Formation

Write the letters and sentences.

F F F F F

Frances flew to France.

Fiona made a friend in Florida.

Felice was her new friend.

1. Pull down straight. Lift.
2. Slide right. Lift.
3. Slide right; stop short.

Letter Formation

Home Practice

Name:

Digital Tutor

Letter Model and Formation

Write the letters and words.

g

g g g g g g g

gallop giant goat growl

gate garage given grape

geese in the garden

Home Practice

Letter Formation

g

1. Circle back all the way around; push up straight. Pull down straight; curve back.

Name: _____

Write the letters and words.

j j j j j j j j

join junk just jump

juice jogged jelly jewel

jar of jam

Letter
Formation

2.
j

j

1. Pull down straight; curve back. Lift.
2. Dot.

Home
Practice

Name:

Digital Tutor

Letter Model and Formation

Write the letters and words.

q

q q q q q q q

queen quick quilt quite

question quart quake quiz

quit quacking

Home Practice **Letter Formation**

q

1. Circle back all the way around; push up straight. Pull down straight; curve forward.

Name: _____

Write the letters and sentences.

G G G G G G G G G

.   .

George met Grant in Georgia.

Geoff called from Germany.

Grace is in Greece.

Letter
Formation

G G   1. Circle back. Slide left.

Home
Practice

Write the letters and sentences.

J J J J J J

J J J J J J

Jack just called Jim.

Is Jay from Jacksonville?

Josh joked with Joyce.

J
1. Pull down straight; curve back. Lift.
2. Slide right.

Name: _____

Digital Tutor

Letter Model
and Formation

Write the letters and sentences.

Q Q Q Q Q Q Q Q

Quick! Come home.

Queen Elizabeth was questioned.

Quiet ducks don't quack.

Letter Formation

1. Circle back all the way around. Lift.
2. Slant right.

Home Practice

Practice Master 37

Name: _____

Write the letters and words.

Digital Tutor

Letter Model
and Formation

Ủ

u u u u u u u u

uncle

unhappy   umbrella

understood   upstairs   upset

up until four

**Home
Practice**

Letter
Formation

Ủ

1. Pull down straight; curve forward; push up.
   Pull down straight.

Practice Master 38

Name: _____

Write the letters and words.

S

s s s s s s s

:

salt   scare   scream   shore

skate   smart   south   speak

seven street signs

Letter Formation   S

Home Practice

1. Curve back; curve forward.

Name: _____

Write the letters and sentences.

U U U U U

U U U U

Uranus is a planet.

Umberto moved to Utah.

Up and away blows the leaf.

U

1. Pull down straight; curve forward; push up.

Name: _____

Write the letters and sentences.

S S S S S S S

S

Sasha knows Sarah's address.

She lives on Sail Street.

Sasha saw Sarah there.

1. Curve back; curve forward.

Letter Formation

S

Name:

Digital Tutor

Letter Model and Formation

Write the letters and words.

b

b b b b b b b

baby belt block beef

barn bean body brush

buy a brown bunny

Home Practice

Letter Formation

b

1. Pull down straight. Push up; circle forward.

Name: _____

Write the letters and words.

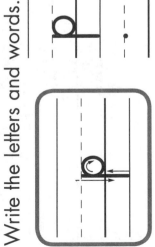

p p p p p p p p

phone   piano   plane

poem   prince   pull   puppy

pick a purple prize

Home Practice

Letter Formation

1. Pull down straight. Push up; circle forward.

Practice Master 43

Name: _____

Write the letters and words.

r r r r r r

radio   ranch   return   rice

round   rush   raise   ran

reach the rusty roof

r

1. Pull down straight. Push up; curve forward.

Name: _____

Write the letters and sentences.

B B B B B B

B B B B B B

Bev works at Bernie's Books.

Books are what she likes best.

Bev also likes to play baseball.

Letter
Formation

1. Pull down straight. Lift.
2. Slide right; curve forward; slide left.
   Slide right; curve forward; slide left.

Home
Practice

Digital Tutor

Letter Model
and Formation

Name:

Digital Tutor

Letter Model and Formation

Write the letters and sentences.

P P P P P P P P

Pru visited her parents.

Pru's parents live in Peru.

Please call your parents.

Home Practice

Letter Formation

P

1. Pull down straight. Lift.
2. Slide right; curve forward; slide left.

Name: _____

Write the letters and sentences.

R R R R R R

R R

Rex named his cat Ralph.

Roy named his rabbit Rena.

Ralph chased Rena.

Digital Tutor

Letter Model
and Formation

Letter
Formation

1. Pull down straight. Lift.
2. Slide right; curve forward; slide left.
   Slant right.

Home
Practice

Practice Master 47

Name:

Write the letters and words.

n n n n n

n n n n

nose nail neck north

nest notice neither net

nap at noon

Letter Formation

n

1. Pull down straight. Push up; curve forward;
   pull down straight.

Digital Tutor

Letter Model and Formation

Name: _____

Write the letters and words.

m m m m m m m m m m

magic   mail   meow   mice

moon   music   movie   mud

make more money

© Zaner-Bloser, Inc.

Digital Tutor

Letter Model and Formation

Letter Formation

m m m

1. Pull down straight. Push up; curve forward; pull down straight. Push up; curve forward; pull down straight.

Home Practice

Practice Master 49

Name: _____

Write the letters and words.

Digital Tutor
Letter Model
and Formation

h   h   h   h   h   h   h

hay   head   honey   hour

hose   hiss   high   huge

her heavy hair

Letter Formation

h

1. Pull down straight. Push up; curve forward; pull down straight.

© Zaner-Bloser, Inc.

Name: _____

Write the letters and sentences.

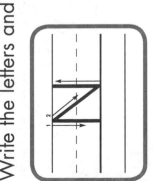

N N N N N N

Niles needs a ride to Nashville.

Neesha is going to Newark.

Now they can share a ride.

Letter
Formation

1. Pull down straight. Lift.
2. Slant right. Push up straight.

Home
Practice

Practice Master 51

Name: _____

Write the letters and sentences.

M M M M M M

M M

Maggie was born in May.

My birthday is in March.

I was born on a Monday.

Letter
Formation

1. Pull down straight. Lift.
2. Slant right. Slant up. Pull down straight.

Name: _____

Write the letters and sentences.

H H H H H H H

Have you heard Harry sing?

He has a scratchy throat.

His throat is sore.

Letter Formation

1. Pull down straight. Lift.
2. Pull down straight. Lift.
3. Slide right.

Home Practice

Name:

Write the letters and words.

v   v   v   v   v   v

van   vine   voice   vase

village   very   violin   vest

visit the valley

V   V

1. Slant right. Slant up.

Name: _____

Write the letters and words.

y y y y y y

y y y

young   yard   you'd

year

yellow   yank   yawn   youth

you'll   say   yes

Practice Master 55

Digital Tutor

Letter Model and Formation

Letter Formation

1. Slant right. Lift.
2. Slant left.

Home Practice

Name: _____

Write the letters and words.

Digital Tutor

Letter Model
and Formation

W   W   W   W   W   W

W   W   W   W   W

wake   week   wheel   win

worm   wrote   worry   wide

wolf walking west

W

1. Slant right. Slant up. Slant right. Slant up.

Name:

Write the letters and sentences.

V V V V V

V V V V V

V

Vinnie ate at the Vine Diner.

Vince bought Vinnie's meal.

Vince lost his voice.

Letter
Formation

1. Slant right. Slant up.

Home
Practice

Name: _____

Write the letters and sentences.

Y Y Y Y Y Y Y

Yesterday was my birthday.

Yanni gave me a gift.

Your gift was nice.

1. Slant right. Lift.
2. Slant left. Pull down straight.

Name: _____

Write the letters and sentences.

W W W W W W

W W W

Wendy went to Winona's house.

Winona lives in Washington.

Where is your house?

Letter
Formation

W

1. Slant right. Slant up. Slant right. Slant up.

Home
Practice

Name: _____

Write the letters and words.

X   X   X   X   X   X   X

next   fix   box   taxes

wax   ax   taxi   sixty

sixteen boxes

1. Slant right. Lift.
2. Slant left.

Name: _____

Write the letters and words.

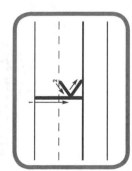

K k k k k k k

key   knee   kiss   knock

knife   park   sock   track

black rocks

Letter Formation

1. Pull down straight. Lift.
2. Slant left. Slant right.

Home Practice

Write the letters and words.

Z

Z   Z   Z   Z   Z

fuzz   zoo   jazz   dizzy

puzzle   zebra   zoom   freeze

a dozen peas

Z

1. Slide right. Slant left. Slide right.

Name: _____

Write the letters and sentences.

X X X X X

X X X X X

Xanthe likes to exercise.

Exercise is good for Xanthe.

There is the Xenia Gym.

Letter
Formation

1. Slant right. Lift.
2. Slant left.

Home
Practice

Name: _____

Write the letters and sentences.

K K K K K K

Kerry walked to school.

She goes to school in Kansas.

Kevin walked with her.

K

1. Pull down straight. Lift.
2. Slant left. Slant right.

Name:

Write the letters and sentences.

Digital Tutor

Letter Model
and Formation

Z

Z Z Z Z

Zelda ordered a pizza.

Pizza is Zelda's favorite food.

Zeus bought Zelda the pizza.

Letter
Formation

 1. Slide right. Slant left. Slide right.

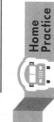
Home
Practice

Name: _____

Digital Tutor

Letter Models
and Formations

Home Practice

Note to Families: In handwriting, we have been writing the letters **l**, **i**, and **t**. Use the models at the bottom of the page to review the formation of these letters with your child. Then spend a few moments completing the activity together. For additional practice, have your child find more words that begin with these letters and write them.

Label each picture with the letter that begins its name.

_____ _____ _____ _____

_____ _____ _____ _____

Letter Formation

1. Pull down straight.

1. Pull down straight. Lift.
2. Dot.

1. Pull down straight. Lift.
2. Slide right.

Name: _____

© Zaner-Bloser, Inc.

Digital Tutor

Letter Models
and Formations

Home
Practice

Note to Families: In handwriting, we have been learning the letters **L**, **I**, and **T**. Review the models at the bottom of the page with your child. To reinforce these letters, spend a few moments completing the activity together. For additional practice, have your child look in an address book or a list of contacts for last names that begin with these letters. Then have your child write the names.

Names

Ivan	Tom	Linda
Linus	Tess	Ida
Ike	Lewis	Tanya

Write each name in the correct column.

Names that begin with L

_____

_____

_____

_____

Names that begin with I

_____

_____

_____

_____

Names that begin with T

_____

_____

_____

_____

Letter Formation

1. Pull down straight.
2. Slide right.

1. Pull down straight. Lift.
2. Slide right. Lift.
3. Slide right.

1. Pull down straight. Lift.
2. Slide right.

Practice Master 67

Name: _____

Digital Tutor
Letter Models
and Formations

Home Practice

Note to Families: In handwriting, we have been learning the letters **o**, **a**, and **d**. Review the models at the bottom of the page with your child. To reinforce these letters, spend a few moments completing the activity together. For additional practice, have your child use his or her finger to write the letters **o**, **a**, and **d** in the air.

Cut out the letter cards. Make textured letters by attaching dry noodles, sand, or glitter with glue. Trace the letters with your finger, following the correct letter formation.

Letter Formation

1. Circle back all the way around.

1. Circle back all the way around; push up straight. Pull down straight.

1. Circle back all the way around; push up straight. Pull down straight.

Name: _____

Home Practice

Note to Families: In handwriting, we have been learning the letters **O, A,** and **D.** Review the models at the bottom of the page with your child. To reinforce these letters, spend a few moments completing the activity together. For additional practice, have your child make letter cards with these letters and place them on items around your home that begin with **O, A,** and **D.**

Trace the shaded letters in the picture. Color the picture.

Letter Formation

 1. Circle back all the way around.

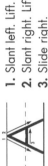 1. Slant left. Lift.
2. Slant right. Lift.
3. Slide right.

 1. Pull down straight. Lift.
2. Slide right; curve forward; slide left.

Practice Master 69

Home Practice

Note to Families: In handwriting, we have been learning the letters **c**, **e**, and **f**. Review the models at the bottom of the page with your child. To reinforce

these letters, spend a few moments completing the activity together. For additional practice, have your child write the name of each item pictured below.

Digital Tutor

Letter Models and Formations

Color the items that begin with **c** orange. Color the items that begin with **e** yellow.
Color the items that begin with **f** blue. Write **c**, **e**, or **f** next to each item.

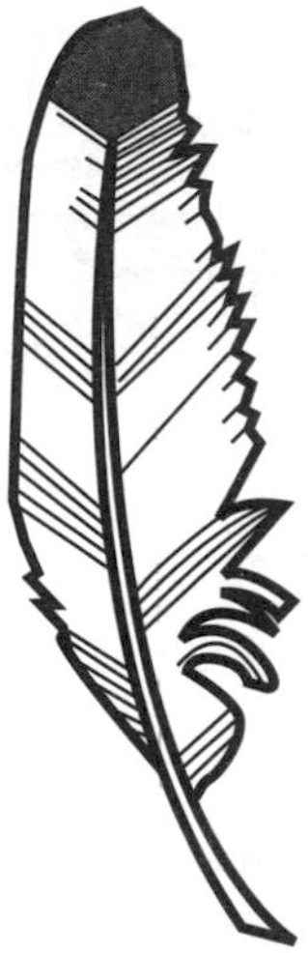

Letter Formation

1. Circle back.

C

1. Slide right. Circle back.

e

1. Curve back; pull down straight. Lift.
2. Slide right.

f

Name: _____

Home Practice

Digital Tutor

Letter Models and Formations

Note to Families: In handwriting, we have been learning the letters **C**, **E**, and **F**. Review the models at the bottom of the page with your child. To reinforce these letters, spend a few moments completing the activity together. For additional practice, have your child write a list of items found outdoors that begin with **C**, **E**, and **F**.

Trace the shaded letters in the picture. Color the picture.

Letter Formation

 1. Circle back.

 1. Pull down straight. Lift.
2. Slide right. Lift. Slide right; stop short. Lift.
3. Slide right.

 1. Pull down straight. Lift.
2. Slide right. Lift. Slide right; stop short.

Practice Master 71

Home Practice

Note to Families: In handwriting, we have been learning the letters **g, j,** and **q.** Review the models at the bottom of the page with your child. To reinforce these letters, spend a few moments completing the activity together. For additional practice, have your child create a letter mobile by writing the letters, cutting them out, and hanging them with string.

Digital Tutor

Letter Models and Formations

Decorate the tree by tracing the letters. Add more of your own.

Letter Formation

1. Circle back all the way around; push up straight. Pull down straight; curve back.

1. Pull down straight; curve back. Lift.
2. Dot.

1. Circle back all the way around; push up straight. Pull down straight; curve forward.

© Zaner-Bloser, Inc.

Name: _____

Digital Tutor

Letter Models
and Formations

Note to Families: In handwriting, we have been learning the letters **G, J,** and **Q.** Review the models at the bottom of the page with your child. To reinforce these letters, spend a few moments completing the activity together. For additional practice, have your child use his or her finger to write the letters **G, J,** and **Q** in the air.

Design the license plates as you like. Use **G, J,** and **Q** in any order, plus any numerals. Color the plates.

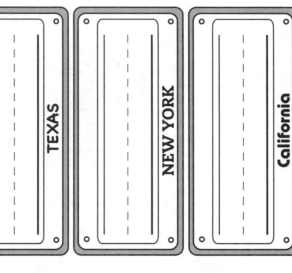

OHIO

TEXAS

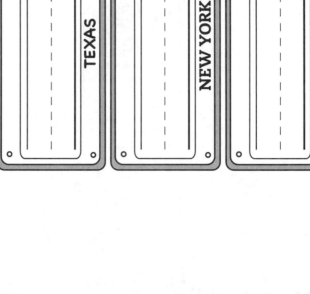

New Jersey

NEW YORK

PENNSYLVANIA

California

**Letter
Formation**

1. Circle back. Slide left.

1. Pull down straight; curve back. Lift.
2. Slide right.

1. Circle back all the way around. Lift.
2. Slant right.

Practice Master 73

Name: _____

Note to Families: In handwriting, we have been learning the letters **u** and **s**. Review the models at the bottom of the page with your child. To reinforce these letters, spend a few moments completing the activity together. For additional practice, have your child change more words by adding **un-** or **-s** to them.

Make the following shaded words plural by adding **-s** at the end of each word. Trace the words.

curl _____

shoe _____

freckle _____

leg _____

Give the following shaded words the opposite meaning by adding **un-** to the beginning of the words. Trace the words.

fold _____

buckle _____

done _____

even _____

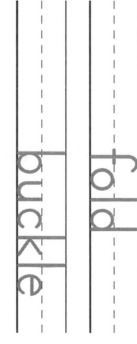

Letter Formation

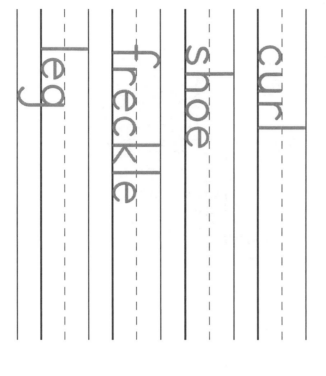
u

1. Pull down straight; curve forward; push up. Pull down straight.

s

1. Curve back; curve forward.

Practice Master 74

© Zaner-Bloser, Inc.

Name: _____

Home Practice

Note to Families: In handwriting, we have been learning the letters **U** and **S**. Review the models at the bottom of the page with your child. To reinforce these letters, spend a few moments completing the activity together. For additional practice, have your child use his or her finger to write the letters **U** and **S** in the air.

Cut out the letter cards. Make textured letters by attaching dry noodles, sand, or glitter with glue. Trace the letters with your finger, following the correct letter formation.

Letter Formation

1. Pull down straight; curve forward; push up.

1. Curve back; curve forward.

Name: _____

Note to Families: In handwriting, we have been learning the letters **b**, **p**, and **r**. Review the models at the bottom of the page with your child. To reinforce these letters, spend a few moments completing the activity together. For additional practice, have your child write a list of items found at home that begin with **b**, **p**, and **r**.

Digital Tutor
Letter Models and Formations

Make a list of items in your classroom that begin with the letters **b**, **p**, and **r**.

Letter Formation

1. Pull down straight. Push up; circle forward.

1. Pull down straight. Push up; circle forward.

1. Pull down straight. Push up; curve forward.

Practice Master 76

© Zaner-Bloser, Inc.

Name: _____

Home Practice

Note to Families: In handwriting, we have been learning the letters **B, P,** and **R.** Review the models at the bottom of the page with your child. To reinforce these letters, spend a few moments completing the activity together. For additional practice, have your child write a note to a friend.

Address the envelope with the following information:

Bruce Bear
741 Reed Road
Purple, RI 52933

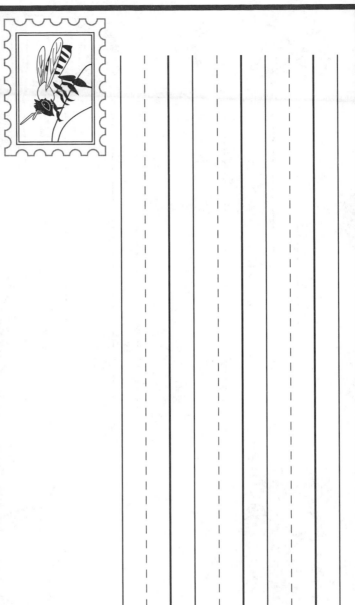

Letter Formation

B 1. Pull down straight. Lift.
   2. Slide right; curve forward; slide left.
   3. Slide right; curve forward; slide left.

P 1. Pull down straight. Lift.
   2. Slide right; curve forward; slide left.

R 1. Pull down straight. Lift.
   2. Slide right; curve forward; slide left.
   3. Slant right.

Practice Master 77

Name: _____

Note to Families: In handwriting, we have been learning the letters **n, m,** and **h.** Review the models at the bottom of the page with your child. To reinforce these letters, spend a few moments completing the activity together. For additional practice, scramble other words that begin with **n, m,** and **h,** and then have your child unscramble them.

Digital Tutor

Letter Models and Formations

Unscramble the letters to form a word. Write the word.

ent

_____

eahd

_____

ath

_____

onom

_____

tsen

_____

Letter Formation

1. Pull down straight. Push up; curve forward; pull down straight.

1. Pull down straight. Push up; curve forward; pull down straight. Push up; curve forward; pull down straight.

1. Pull down straight. Push up; curve forward; pull down straight.

Name: _____

Digital Tutor

Letter Models and Formations

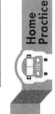

Home Practice

Note to Families: In handwriting, we have been learning the letters **N**, **M**, and **H**. Review the models at the bottom of the page with your child. To reinforce these letters, spend a few moments completing the activity together. For additional practice, have your child use his or her finger to write the letters **N**, **M**, and **H** in the air.

Trace the shaded letters in the picture. Color the picture.

Letter Formation

1. Pull down straight. Lift.
2. Slant right. Push up straight.

1. Pull down straight. Lift.
2. Slant right. Slant up. Pull down straight.

1. Pull down straight. Lift.
2. Pull down straight. Lift.
3. Slide right.

Practice Master 79

Name: _____

Note to Families: In handwriting, we have been learning the letters **v**, **y**, and **w**. Review the models at the bottom of the page with your child. To reinforce these letters, spend a few moments completing the activity together. For additional practice, have your child write words that begin with **v**, **y**, and **w**.

Digital Tutor

Letter Models
and Formations

Write the letters with a dark crayon or marker. Then use other colors to draw letter creatures.

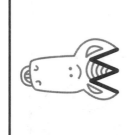

Letter Formation

1. Slant right. Slant up.

1. Slant right. Lift.
2. Slant left.

1. Slant right. Slant up.
Slant right. Slant up.

Name: _____

Digital Tutor

Letter Models
and Formations

Home Practice

Note to Families: In handwriting, we have been learning the letters **V, Y,** and **W.** Review the models at the bottom of the page with your child. To reinforce these letters, spend a few moments completing the activity together. For additional practice, have your child write names of people that begin with **V, Y,** and **W** in appropriate columns.

Word Box

Yankton	Walnut	Valdez	York
Waldron	Vinton	Yosemite	Wells
Vail	Wahoo	Vermont	Yucca

Write the name of each place in the correct column.

V places

Y places

W places

Letter Formation

1. Slant right. Slant up.

1. Slant right. Lift.
2. Slant left. Pull down straight.

1. Slant right. Slant up. Slant right. Slant up.

Practice Master 81

Home Practice

Note to Families: In handwriting, we have been learning the letters **x**, **k**, and **z**. Review the models at the bottom of the page with your child. To reinforce these letters, spend a few moments completing the activity together. For additional practice, help your child change letters in other words to create new words. Have them write the new words.

Digital Tutor
Letter Models and Formations

Change the shaded letter or letters in each word to **x**, **k**, or **z** to make a new word. Write the new word.

hive _____ funny _____ cool _____

hero _____ neat _____ fit _____

fob _____ loop _____ room _____

Letter Formation

1. Slant right. Lift.
2. Slant left.

1. Pull down straight. Lift.
2. Slant left. Slant right.

1. Slide right. Slant left. Slide right.

Name:

Digital Tutor

Letter Models
and Formations

Home Practice

Note to Families: In handwriting, we have been learning the letters **X, K,** and **Z.** Review the models at the bottom of the page with your child. To reinforce these letters, spend a few moments completing the activity together. For additional practice, have your child use his or her finger to write the letters **X, K,** and **Z** in the air.

Design the license plates as you like. Use **X, K,** and **Z** in any order, plus any numerals. Color the plates.

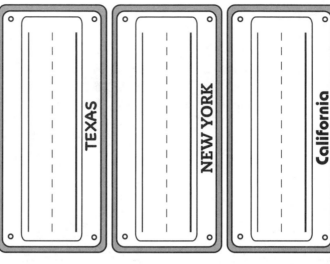

OHIO

TEXAS

New Jersey

NEW YORK

PENNSYLVANIA

California

Letter Formation

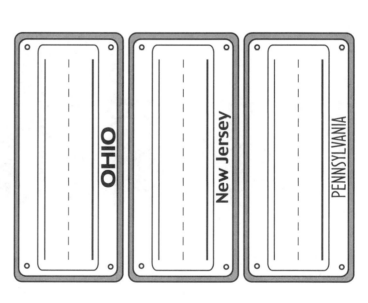

1. Slant right. Lift.
2. Slant left.

1. Pull down straight. Lift.
2. Slant left. Slant right.

1. Slide right. Slant left. Slide right.

Practice Master 83

Record of Student's Handwriting Skills

Manuscript

	Needs Improvement	Shows Mastery
Uses good sitting position	☐	☐
Positions paper correctly	☐	☐
Holds pencil correctly	☐	☐
Writes vertical lines	☐	☐
Writes horizontal lines	☐	☐
Writes circle lines	☐	☐
Writes diagonal lines	☐	☐
Writes numerals **1–10**	☐	☐
Writes **l, i,** and **t**	☐	☐
Writes **L, I,** and **T**	☐	☐
Writes **o, a,** and **d**	☐	☐
Writes **O, A,** and **D**	☐	☐
Writes **c, e,** and **f**	☐	☐
Writes **C, E,** and **F**	☐	☐
Writes **g, j,** and **q**	☐	☐
Writes **G, J,** and **Q**	☐	☐

	Needs Improvement	Shows Mastery
Writes **u** and **s**	☐	☐
Writes **U** and **S**	☐	☐
Writes **b, p,** and **r**	☐	☐
Writes **B, P,** and **R**	☐	☐
Writes **n, m,** and **h**	☐	☐
Writes **N, M,** and **H**	☐	☐
Writes **v, y,** and **w**	☐	☐
Writes **V, Y,** and **W**	☐	☐
Writes **x, k,** and **z**	☐	☐
Writes **X, K,** and **Z**	☐	☐
Writes with correct shape	☐	☐
Writes with correct size	☐	☐
Writes with correct spacing	☐	☐
Writes with correct slant	☐	☐
Regularly checks written work for legibility	☐	☐

Zaner-Bloser
Handwriting
▶

Certificate of Excellence

Awarded to

_____

In recognition of outstanding excellence toward the goals and standards set forth in the Zaner-Bloser Handwriting Program.

Given this _____ day of _____ , 20____ .

_____
Teacher/Principal

_____
School

_____
Grade

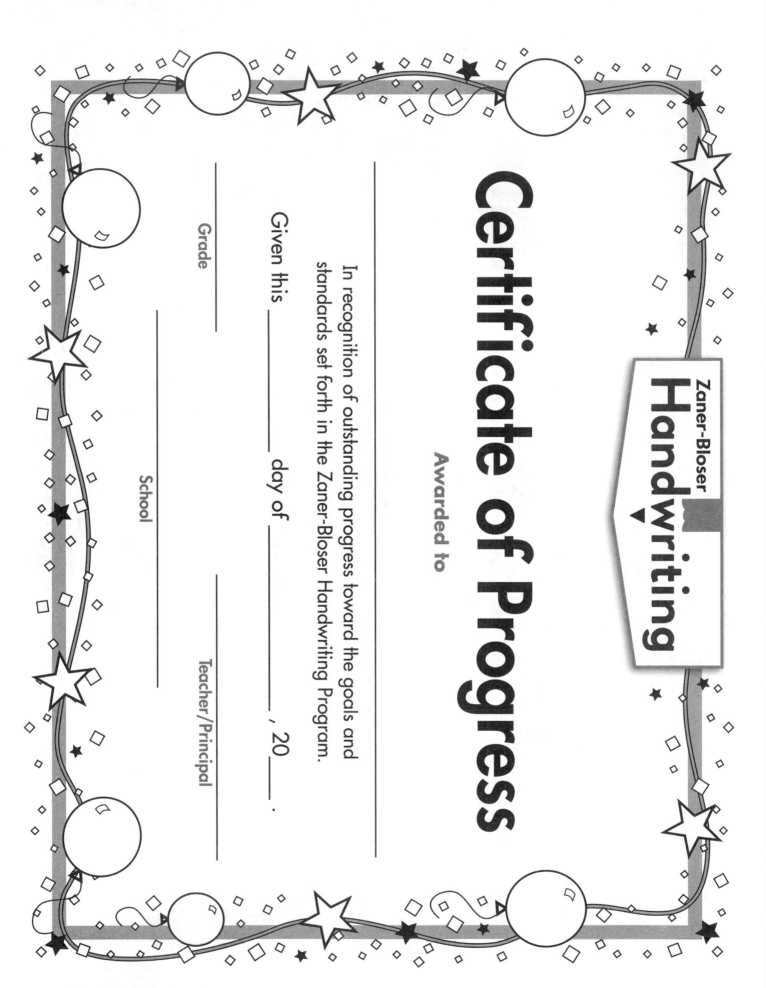

Zaner-Bloser

Handwriting

Certificate of Progress

Awarded to

In recognition of outstanding progress toward the goals and standards set forth in the Zaner-Bloser Handwriting Program.

Given this _____ day of _____ , 20 ___ .

Grade

School

Teacher/Principal

Manuscript Alphabet

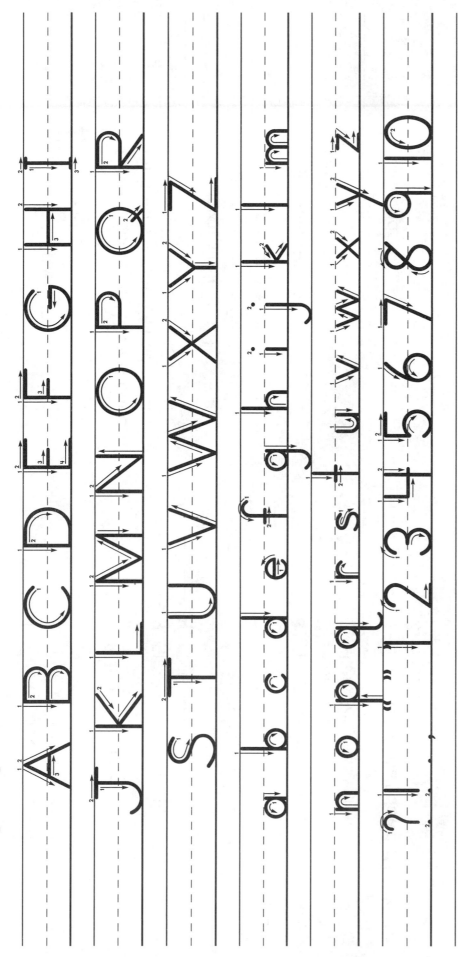

Manuscript Letter and Numeral Formations

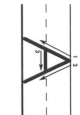

1. Slant left. Lift.
2. Slant right. Lift.
3. Slide right.

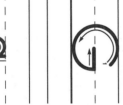

1. Circle back all the way around; push up straight. Pull down straight.

1. Pull down straight. Lift.
2. Slide right; curve forward; slide left. Slide right; curve forward; slide left.

1. Pull down straight. Push up; circle forward.

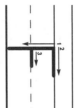

1. Circle back.

1. Pull down straight. Lift.
2. Slide right; curve forward; slide left.

1. Circle back all the way around; push up straight. Pull down straight.

1. Pull down straight. Lift.
2. Slide right. Lift.
3. Slide right; stop short. Lift.
4. Slide right.

1. Slide right. Circle back.

1. Curve back; pull down straight. Lift.
2. Slide right. Lift.
3. Slide right; stop short.

1. Pull down straight. Lift.
2. Slide right.

1. Circle back. Slide left.

1. Circle back all the way around; push up straight. Pull down straight; curve back.

1. Pull down straight. Slide right.

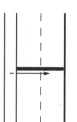

1. Pull down straight.

1. Pull down straight. Lift.
2. Slant right. Slant up. Pull down straight.

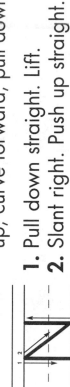

1. Pull down straight. Push up; curve forward; pull down straight. Push up; curve forward; pull down straight.

1. Pull down straight. Lift.
2. Slant right. Push up straight.

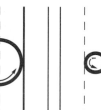

1. Pull down straight. Push up; curve forward; pull down straight.

1. Circle back all the way around.

1. Circle back all the way around.

1. Pull down straight. Lift.
2. Pull down straight. Lift.
3. Slide right.

1. Pull down straight. Push up; curve forward; pull down straight.

1. Pull down straight. Lift.
2. Slide right. Lift.
3. Slide right.

1. Pull down straight. Lift.
2. Dot.

1. Pull down straight; curve back. Lift.
2. Slide right.

1. Pull down straight; curve back. Lift.
2. Dot.

1. Pull down straight. Lift.
2. Slant left. Slant right.

1. Pull down straight. Lift.
2. Slant left. Slant right.

Practice Master 89

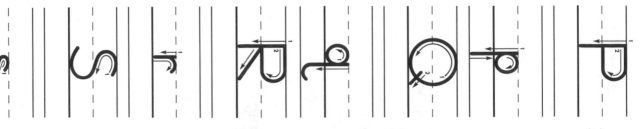
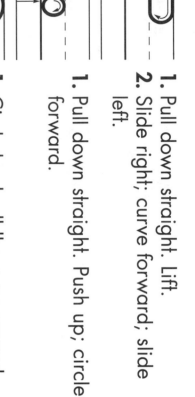

P
1. Pull down straight. Lift.
2. Slide right; curve forward; slide left.

T
1. Pull down straight. Lift.
2. Slide right.

p
1. Pull down straight. Push up; circle forward.

U
1. Pull down straight; curve forward; push up.

O
1. Circle back all the way around.

u
1. Pull down straight; curve forward; push up. Pull down straight.

q
1. Circle back all the way around; push up straight. Pull down straight; curve forward.
2. Slant right.

V
1. Slant right. Slant up.

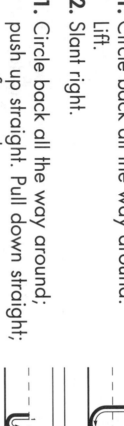
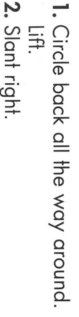

R
1. Pull down straight. Lift.
2. Slide right; curve forward; slide left. Slant right.

v
1. Slant right. Slant up.

r
1. Pull down straight. Push up; curve forward.

W
1. Slant right. Slant up. Slant right. Slant up.

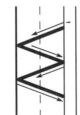
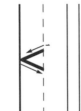
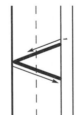

S
1. Curve back; curve forward.

s
1. Curve back; curve forward.

w
1. Slant right. Slant up. Slant right. Slant up.

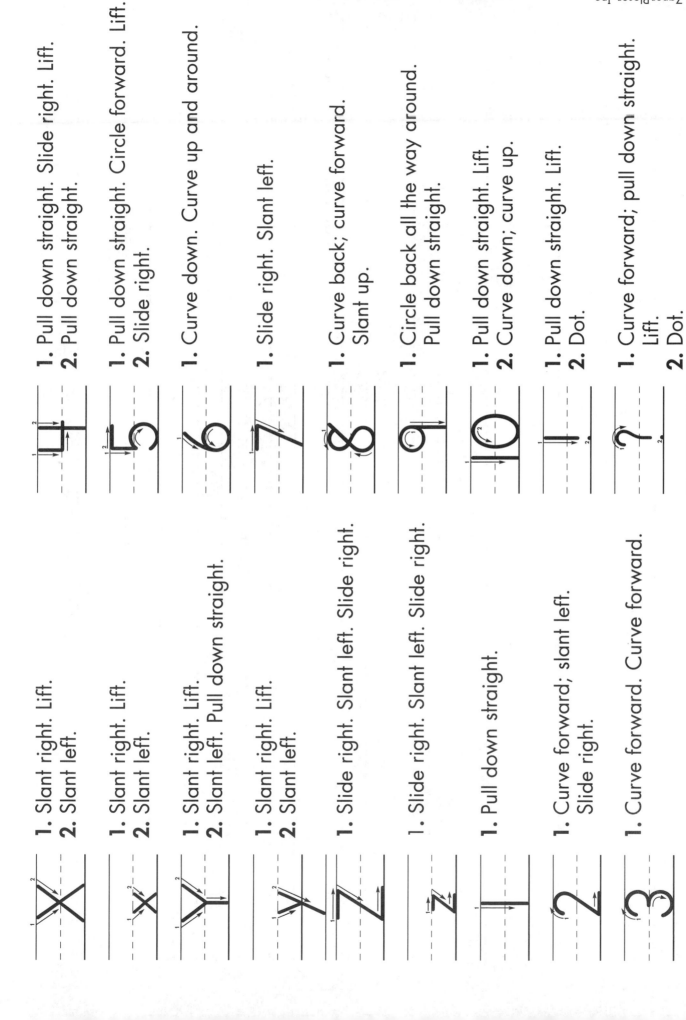

4
1. Pull down straight. Slide right. Lift.
2. Pull down straight.

5
1. Pull down straight. Circle forward. Lift.
2. Slide right.

6
1. Curve down. Curve up and around.

7
1. Slide right. Slant left.

8
1. Curve back; curve forward. Slant up.

9
1. Circle back all the way around. Pull down straight.

10
1. Pull down straight. Lift.
2. Curve down; curve up.

!
1. Pull down straight. Lift.
2. Dot.

?
1. Curve forward; pull down straight. Lift.
2. Dot.

X
1. Slant right. Lift.
2. Slant left.

x
1. Slant right. Lift.
2. Slant left.

Y
1. Slant right. Lift.
2. Slant left. Pull down straight.

k
1. Slant right. Lift.
2. Slant left.

N
1. Slide right. Slant left. Slide right.

z
1. Slide right. Slant left. Slide right.

T
1. Pull down straight.

2
1. Curve forward; slant left. Slide right.

3
1. Curve forward. Curve forward.

Story-Writing Grid